'Again, again!' must be the enduring memory of any person who has had the privilege to read aloud to young children. Well-loved stories that are requested over and over, until such time that the tale can be recited by heart.

And so starts our earliest journey into literacy and language – cherished memories of choosing a story with care, being lifted to a special lap for snuggles and undivided attention as a new adventure unfolds.

Over many years of observation and research we've come to know that laughter, smiles and eye contact form the basis of the very best part of cognitive development, providing a platform for peak learning experiences. One of the simplest tools to support this platform is that of baby signing – or gesture communication – in conjunction with speech. It is, without doubt, the bridge between communication and language.

Sign language has obvious benefits for those with hearing difficulties but it also provides wonderful connection and understanding for everyone, from babyhood onwards. It provides support for toddlers with emerging speech and adds layers of learning for older children. Using wonderful books (like the 'Rhyme and Sign' Adventure series) provides the perfect vehicle for enhanced interactions, language and communication skills. Signing is quite literally 'language in motion' and, as children learn best by doing, it helps them to learn more ably, retain information and recall it more easily.

Out of My Window is our third in the award winning 'Rhyme and Sign' Adventure series; we've been sure to include all of those things you loved so much when reading **Our Farmyard Friends** and **At the Bottom of My Garden**. A rhyming and repetitive story line (enabling little ones to join in easily), beautiful illustrations (we invite you to spot the surprise additions!) and the enjoyment you will get from signing will mean that this too becomes a much-loved tale in your library - returned to time and again.

From us, to you, with love.

Always say
Sign in your l
Repeat

529 980 22 9

"This is a lovely story in its own right but it's actually much more than that.

There's lots of rhyme and repetition which are important for supporting language learning and developing vocabulary - plus the addition of signs which can help enhance early literacy and learning.

You don't need any signing experience to be able to use this book straight away. It's an accessible and enjoyable tale for all ages from babies to grandparents.

They'll all love to join in!"

Libby Hill
Consultant Speech and Language Therapist
Small Talk Speech and Language Therapy

Getting the most out of your 'Rhyme and Sign' Adventure

You don't need to sign every word
When signing to songs with young children pick a sign or two per sentence. They love to join in and feel capable – too many signs in a sentence will feel overwhelming as their little hands will struggle to join in.

Slow it down
Being mindful of little fingers, slow down. It might feel strange at first to speak more slowly but the children will be able to engage more fully. As you sign, look to see any attempt to join in. Wait for a moment or two and then move on to the next part. This allows everyone to join in and will reduce frustration about missing the next sign or part of the story whilst concentrating on something prior.

Be dramatic and engaging
Many signs are accompanied by over-exaggerated facial expressions. Its good to practise this with little people as they really get involved with stories with their whole bodies. It will help with identification of feelings - and for those children who find emotions of others difficult to define, it can add a new understanding.

Enable everyone to join in
Signing stories in English word order means that there are more frequent visual cues for young children; they can anticipate what is happening and are able to join in more easily.

Frequent repetition
You'll have found that young children like to hear their favourite stories over and over again. When using signing, stories are absorbed more readily and the signs will quickly become a natural part of their communication.

Attention and Observation
We've added some surprise additions throughout the book and these invite children of all ages to spend time observing what they see. You'll have huge fun together whilst your little one develops their attention and observation abilities - critical pre-reading and literacy skills.

Facilitate more effective learning
Children are kinaesthetic learners which means that they learn more ably when they are involved with what they are doing. Signing is literally 'language in motion' and using signs with favourite stories helps to:

✓ promote better communication
✓ builds a larger word bank
   ✓ facilitate more effective learning
✓ increase confidence
✓ improve literacy skills

Helpful Tips for Hand Shapes

Bunched Hand
The finger ends and thumb are all bunched together.

Bent Hand
The fingers are together and straight, then bent at the palm knuck[le]

Closed Hand
The hand is closed with thumb against index finger.

Full C Hand
The thumb is curv[ed] and the fingers ar[e] together, curved i[n] C shape.

Flat Hand
Hand is held flat with all fingers straight and together.

Full O Hand
The tips of fingers and thumb are hel[d] together to form a[n] O shape.

Clawed Hand
The fingers are extended and bent, spread apart.

V Hand
The index and middle fingers are extended and spre[ad] apart.

Core Signs Glossary

We've split our book into two parts; the **core** signs that we suggest that you sign throughout the book and the **supplementary** signs (which you will find at the back of the book) that you may like to use with older children, or when you are more familiar with the core signs.

You'll find the sign graphics are repeated, in the order in which they are used, on the relevant pages to give you a handy visual reminder along the way.

Little ones will love to join in with finding the correct sign for you and delight in showing you their ability to sign for themselves.

Aeroplane
Closed hand, with thumb and little finger extended, moves in action of flying a plane.

Ambulance
Full 'O' hand held upright makes repeated opening movements as it swivels round at the wrist (mimics flashing light).

Bicycle
Closed hands make alternate forward circular motions.

Boat
Tips of flat hands touch at an angle then move up and down in a bobbing motion (as if moving over water).

Bus
(see Lorry)
Fingers of bent 'V' hand make short movement downwards, twice, at shoulder height.

Car
Closed hands move in the action of holding and moving a steering wheel.

Fire Engine
Fingers of palm facing hands wiggle as hands move upwards (fire) palm up fists make wide flat steering movements.

Look
'V' hand (eye gaze classifier) makes a short movement forward or in the direction to suit the context.

Lorry/Truck*
Palm up fists make wide flat steering movements.
*Is also used for Bus.

Police Car
Fingers of right 'V' hand draw across the back of left wrist, as if denoting stripes (police) then fists move as if steering a car.

Road
'N' hands or flat hands, held apart, flex from the wrists to point and move forwards.

Sea
Palm down open hand moves sideways in wavy up and down motion.

Sky
Flat hand, palms down, move apart in an arc above the head.

Tractor
Palm up fists make wide flat steering movements as body /shoulders shake up and down.

Train
Closed hand makes a firm forward circular movement from side of body.

We're off on a train - hip hip hooray!
We're all ready for a busy day.

Train

Day

We've got a packed lunch and something for tea;
look out of the window - what will we see?

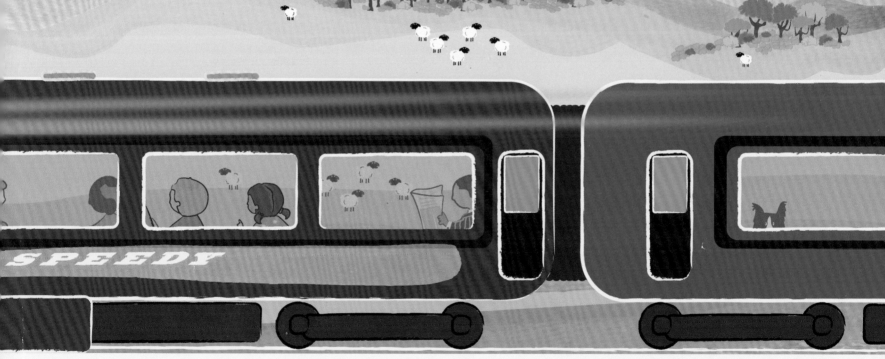

Lunch / Tea

Look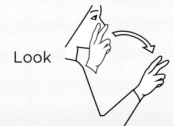

Clickety clack, clackety click...
Look out of my window -
quick, quick, quick!

Look

Quick

I spy, with my little eye, journeys on roads, the sea and the sky.

Road

Sea

Sky

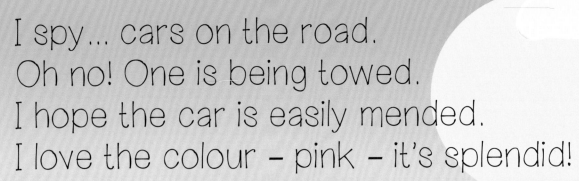

I spy... cars on the road.
Oh no! One is being towed.
I hope the car is easily mended.
I love the colour – pink – it's splendid!

Car

Mended

I spy... lorries stuck in a queue.
The drivers wave and try to view
the reason for the traffic jam –
making sure their brakes don't slam!

Lorry

Traffic Jam

I spy, with my little eye,
journeys on roads, the sea and the sky.

Sky

Car

Lorry

I spy... a racing blue light,
I really hope everything is all right.
A police car races along the street
to help their police friends on the beat.

Blue

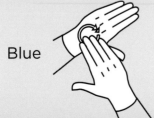

Police Car

I spy... a fire engine; shiny and red!
The traffic moves over
so it gets ahead.
The sirens are loud;
'Nee Nah' they scream
as the brave firefighters
rush to the scene.

Fire Engine

Brave

I spy, with my little eye, journeys on roads, the sea and the sky.

Sky

Fire Engine

Motorbike

I spy... an ambulance on the way
to help someone and save the day.
The siren wails and lights flash bright,
through the day and through the night.

EMERGENCY AMBULANCE

GIVE WAY

Ambulance

Help

I spy... up high in the sky –
a plane with it's passengers waving bye-bye.

It's taking people on holidays
and flying through the sun's
bright rays.

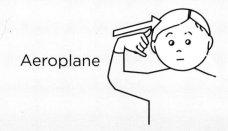

Aeroplane

Holiday

Clickety clack, clackety click...
Look out of my window -
quick, quick, quick!

Look Quick Road Sea

I spy, with my little eye, journeys on roads, the sea and the sky.

Sky

Aeroplane

Helicopter

I spy... the cycle path.
Wow it's so muddy - they all need a bath!
Riding their bikes over hills and grass,
peddling hard, going so fast!

Bicycle

Fast

I spy... a tractor chugging away.
The farmer is busy working all day.
Over the fields and along the track
the animals are safe, right there in the back.

Tractor

Animals

I spy, with my little eye,
journeys on roads, the sea and the sky.

Sky

Tractor

Helicopter

I spy... a bright red bus.
Away around town, without any fuss.
Ding! Ding! goes the bell; the bus stops.
People get off and head to the shops.

Bus

Stop

I spy... the bustling quay.
Look at the boats, way out at sea!
Sit down here and swinging our feet,
we'll enjoy our ice-cream treat!

Boat

Ice-cream

Clickety clack, clackety click...
Back on the train -
quick, quick, quick!

| Train | Quick | Home | Aeroplane | Arnbulance | Bicycle | Boat |

We're homeward bound –
it's been such a long day...
Can you remember what we saw
on the way?

Bus   Car   Fire Engine   Lorry   Police Car   Tractor

Supplementary Signs Glossary

This book has been designed to grow with your little one and, as they become adept with basic signs, they will soon want to know more and more! If you have started to read this story with toddlers or older children, don't be surprised if they pick up signing very quickly indeed, sometimes immediately.

Include these signs once you feel comfortable with the core signs – or if your child is older and wants to learn more – but please don't feel overwhelmed.

Help You
Closed hands with thumb up rests on left palm as hands move forward together in a small arc.

Help
You may find ASL easier for babies and young toddlers to manage. Flat hands tap chest twice.

Animals
'Clawed' hands make repeated alternate forward circular movements.

Blue*
Fingers of right hand rub in small circles on back or palm of left hand.
*Colours vary widely.

Brave
Tips of clawed hands on upper chest then hands move firmly forward closing to fists (can be one handed).

Day
Palm back open hands near face start crossed then swing apart and upwards.

Holiday
Flat hands at sides of head move slightly down and apart, twisting to palm forward.

Home
Tips of flat hands touch, with hands held at an angle.

Ice Cream
Fist makes repeated brushing downwards movements near mouth, tongue slightly out.

Lunch/Tea
Bunched hand makes two short movements to the mouth.

Mended
Edge of right fist bangs top of left fist in circular movements.

Quick/Fast
Right index finger bangs sharply on left and bounces back up again.

Stops
Palm forward flat hand (or both hands) makes a short firm movement forward.

Traffic jam
Palm down flat hands. Left hand in front of right. Right hand moves back in several small hops.